STAGE 1

EARTH AND SKY

BY ALI SPARKES AND JOANNA NADIN

**ILLUSTRATED BY CHLOE DOUGLASS,
ADRIANA SANTOS AND MARTIN BUSTAMANTE**

OXFORD
UNIVERSITY PRESS

CONTENTS

BRILLIANT BROTHER

BY ALI SPARKES
ILLUSTRATED BY CHLOE DOUGLASS

BEFORE READING

Setting the scene
Families come in all shapes and sizes but some things are nearly always true: little brothers can sometimes be annoying and parents can sometimes be embarrassing. That's certainly the case in Frankie's family.

Prepare to read
Read page 7. Can you work out what is happening at the beginning of this story?

Use the expert tips:

■ **Visualize – form a picture in your mind**
Imagine waking up and seeing a giant eye looking at you. How would you feel? What would you do?

■ **Predict** Who do you think the eye might belong to?

Challenge word
whooped
Find this word on page 14. Can you work out what it means?

BRILLIANT BROTHER

Chapter 1

Frankie had an unusual family – they were sometimes odd, but often funny. His little brother Barry, though, was *always* annoying.

One Saturday, Frankie woke up with a giant eye hovering over him.

He screamed.

"Ssshhh," said the giant eye. "You'll make me lose count."

"GET OFF!" yelled Frankie.

"Keep STILL!" ordered the giant eye. "I'm nearly finished."

The giant floating eye was Barry's. He was looking at Frankie through the lens of his magnifying glass.

Frankie shoved his brother off his bed. Barry landed with a thud.

"You've RUINED it!" he wailed. "I was up to one hundred and twelve!"

"One hundred and twelve WHAT?" snapped Frankie.

"Eyelashes!" Barry shouted back. "The average human has 70 to 150 lashes on the upper eyelid. I was checking!"

Frankie groaned. Barry was obsessed with very tiny things – like eyelashes – or huge things, like planets. If he wasn't peering at a greenfly through his magnifying glass, he was staring into the sky with his binoculars.

"Count your OWN eyelashes!" muttered Frankie. "Argh. *Why* have we got to share a bedroom?"

Frankie glanced round the room. On the floor there was a jumbled mess of socks and trainers. Barry's books about space took up over half of the bookshelves, and his collection of binoculars, magnifying glasses and microscopes covered the desk.

"This bedroom *would* be big enough for both of us ..." said Barry, "... if it was in space. If we had zero gravity, we could float up and use the area *above* the floor."

"Or YOU could go into space and I'd have this room!" snapped Frankie.

The day didn't get any better. Here are five ways Barry annoyed Frankie:

1. All the way to the park he watched the sky through his binoculars, hoping to see a meteor.

2. He messed up a football game. He was meant to be in goal, but he was too busy looking at an ants' nest through his magnifying glass.

3. He told the ice-cream seller that his 'Rocket' ice lollies were badly designed, and would never get off the ground if they were actually sent into space.

4. He told a bunch of little kids that the Earth could get hit by a giant asteroid in their lifetime ... and made them cry.

5. On the way home he went on *forever* about how Jupiter is two and a half times bigger than all the other planets in the solar system put together.

ICE CREAMS

Barry didn't mean to be annoying – he just didn't think the same way as everyone else. Frankie could usually put up with it. At least, he *thought* he could. But then Mum called him into the kitchen, and things started to get worse.

Mum was making marmalade. A huge pot of it was bubbling on the stove like orange lava.

"I can't leave my marmalade!" she said. "But I said I'd take Barry to the fair."

"Oh no ..." said Frankie.

"So can *you* take him, when you go with your friends?" asked Mum. She held up a spoon of steaming, gooey marmalade and peered at it. "Looking GOOD!" she whooped.

She didn't even hear Frankie wailing: "NOOOOOOOOO!"

BRILLIANT BROTHER

Chapter 2

BEFORE READING

Prepare to read

At the end of Chapter 1, did you predict that Frankie would take his brother to the fair?

Check your predictions by reading the first page of Chapter 2. Did you predict correctly?

Use the expert tip:

- **Explore vocabulary – clarify words and phrases**
Find the word on page 17 that describes how Frankie spoke to Barry. What does that tell you about how Frankie was feeling and his attitude towards Barry?

Challenge word
droning
Find this word on page 18. Can you work out what it means?

Chapter 2

Frankie and Barry were at the fair with Frankie's friends, Will and Rosi. It was late afternoon and the fairground was crowded. Loud music blared all around.

"A candyfloss contains 30 grams of sugar–" said Barry.

"Just eat it, Barry," growled Frankie.

"If you tried eating this in space, it could be dangerous," Barry went on, waving the pink fluffy cloud of candyfloss. "It's so light, it could float away and clog up the air vents in a space station."

"Just EAT it!" snapped Frankie, while Rosi and Will snorted with laughter.

Barry kept droning on as he rode his painted horse up and down on the carousel.

All of a sudden, Barry's candyfloss flew off the stick and smacked into the face of a lady standing nearby. She was still trying to get all the pink sticky fluff out of her hair when they got off the ride.

"The way to get rid of sticky substances," declared Barry, "is to freeze them and–"

The woman was looking very confused, so Frankie, Will and Rosi dragged Barry away.

"Let's go on the helter-skelter," said Rosi. "Barry can't get us into trouble on *that!*"

Rosi was wrong. At the top of the helter-skelter tower, Barry refused to go down the slide.

"What is it?" asked Will. "Did you forget your mat?"

"No," said Barry, getting out his binoculars. "Look, we can see the moon even though it's the afternoon. I want to see it properly."

Frankie groaned. Other children were jamming up on the stairs behind them. "Barry! Go DOWN the slide!" yelled Frankie.

"I can't," said Barry, suddenly pointing the binoculars downward. "There's a person moving suspiciously in the crowd."

Then, just as Frankie was about to shove his brother down the slide, there was a scream from below.

"He grabbed my bag!" It was the lady with candyfloss in her hair. A man was running away, scattering the crowd.

Barry stood with his binoculars stuck to his eyes for another two minutes. Then he disappeared down the slide. Frankie slid down after him. He found Barry using a borrowed mobile phone.

"What are you *doing?*" Frankie hissed.

Barry was giving information to the police. "He was around two metres tall, of slim build and running to the south exit of the fair," said Barry.

"He got into a blue estate car. He'll be driving north along Pool Street. The car's registration number is W567 TJ8. Yes, I'm sure. I saw it all though my ultra-high magnification binoculars."

Will and Rosi arrived. All three just stood and stared while Barry guided the police patrol car straight to the blue estate car. The bag-snatcher was arrested on the spot.

Twenty minutes later, Candy Floss Hair Lady had her bag back, and Barry was talking to an admiring police officer.

"You have to admit Barry can be brilliant sometimes," said Will, as they walked home.

"Yeah – I suppose," said Frankie.

"No one has ever committed a crime in space," Barry announced. "But if they did–"

"NOOOOOOOOOOOOOO!" wailed Frankie.

Amazing Telescopes

BY ALI SPARKES

BEFORE READING

Setting the scene

We have read about the Moon, but have you ever wondered how we know so much about the Moon and outer space? For more than four hundred years, people have been developing ways to see further and further into space so that we can investigate the universe.

Prepare to read

Why are telescopes important for investigating our universe?

Use the expert tip:

- **Summarize the text** Look for facts to help you answer this question while you are reading this text.

Challenge word

robotic
Find this word on page 32. Can you work out what it means?

Amazing Telescopes

Since ancient times, people have gazed into the night sky, fascinated by twinkling stars and planets.

Until the early 17th Century, people had only seen planets and stars with their eyes. Then, in 1608, the first telescope was invented by Hans Lippershey. He used curved glass lenses to make objects look bigger.

An early telescope

Galileo

In 1609, an Italian called Galileo made an even better telescope. Using his telescope, he showed that the planets in our solar system travel round the Sun. Many people at that time thought the Sun and all the planets travelled round the Earth, because they believed the Earth was the centre of everything. Galileo was arrested for explaining that it wasn't!

Galileo was the first to discover the planet Jupiter's four moons.

Jupiter is a giant planet. It's so huge you could fit more than 1300 Earths into it.

Learning through telescopes

Since Galileo's time, astronomers have used better and better telescopes to learn more about planets.

The smallest planet is Mercury. If the Earth was a tennis ball, Mercury would look like a marble next to it.

We used to think Pluto was our smallest planet, but in recent years astronomers have decided it is a 'dwarf planet' because it is too small to be a proper planet.

Powerful telescopes

Amazing new telescopes were developed during the 20th and 21st Centuries. In 1957, a huge telescope was built in the UK at Jodrell Bank in Cheshire. The **Lovell Telescope** is 89 metres high and looks like a giant white dish on a frame. It can be mechanically twisted around and pointed into any part of the sky. It has been upgraded over the years. You can go to the Jodrell Bank visitor centre and see it.

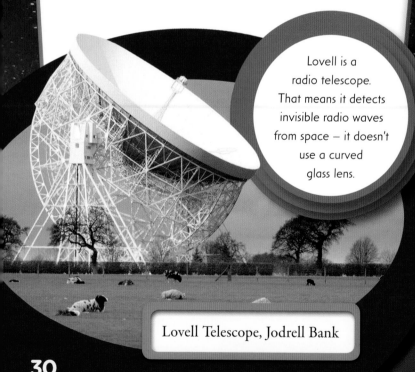

Lovell is a radio telescope. That means it detects invisible radio waves from space – it doesn't use a curved glass lens.

Lovell Telescope, Jodrell Bank

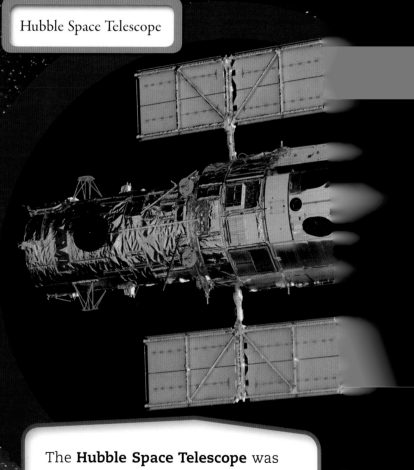

Hubble Space Telescope

The **Hubble Space Telescope** was launched into space in 1990. Hubble takes pictures of stars, planets and galaxies as it whirls around the Earth at about 17 000 miles per hour.

Space telescope give us very clear v of stars and planets be they are away from Earth's atmosphere. means our weather d interfere with them

Probes

In the 21st Century, we're now sending probes into deep space, so we can find out about planets far away. A space probe is a robotic spacecraft that explores space and sends data back to Earth.

NASA launched the probe, *New Horizons*, in 2006.

New Horizons

NASA is the USA's National Aeronautics and Space Administration. It aims to answer questions such as: what is out there in space and how do we get there?

Pluto

In 2015, *New Horizons* reached Pluto and sent back amazing images. They showed us that the dwarf planet has a vast heart-shaped glacier measuring over 1600 kilometres across. We also now know that Pluto's atmosphere is blue.

Pluto

heart-shaped glacier

Pluto's moon

Images from *New Horizons* have also shown us that Pluto's moon, Charon, has a dark red cap. Scientists think this might be gas that has escaped from Pluto's atmosphere.

dark red cap

Pluto's moon, Charon

Scientists hope that *New Horizons* will continue its journey through space and send back more data from worlds at the edge of our solar system. We have come a long way from those early telescopes – but most of the universe is still to be explored!

Amazing Earthquakes

BY JOANNA NADIN

BEFORE READING

Setting the scene

We often hear about earthquakes on the news and see pictures of the devastation they can cause. Have you ever wondered why earthquakes happen? This information text will help you find all sorts of facts about earthquakes.

Prepare to read

Read page 37.

Use the expert tip:

■ **Ask a question** What would you like to find out about earthquakes?

Challenge word

colossal

Find this word on page 42. What do you think it means?

Amazing
Earthquakes

What is an earthquake?

Earthquakes happen when pressure builds up under the surface of the earth. A large earthquake can make the ground shake violently, cracking rocks and sometimes destroying roads and buildings.

Earthquake in Amatrice, Italy, August 2016

How are earthquakes measured?

The strength, or magnitude, of an earthquake is measured using a **seismometer**. These machines can sense **vibrations** within the ground.

There are several hundred earthquakes recorded in the UK each year, but only around twenty to thirty of these can be felt. An earthquake has to have a magnitude of 2.5 before it can be felt by humans.

We measure earthquake vibrations using scales. One such scale is the Richter scale. Earthquakes are given a number from 0–10 on the Richter scale.

To give you an idea of the strength of a big earthquake, the world's biggest nuclear bomb had a magnitude of just over 8.0.

In the UK, the biggest recorded quake was in 1931 and had a magnitude of 6.1. Luckily, it was more than 96 km off the coast so it didn't cause much damage!

How often do earthquakes happen?

There are an estimated 500 000 earthquakes around the world every year. However, only around 100 000 of those can actually be felt, and about 100 cause actual damage.

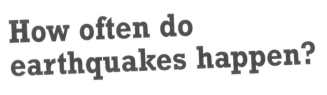

Earthquake in Khokana, Nepal, 2015

Don't panic! Around the world we only get around twenty big earthquakes (measuring 7.0 or more) every year. Massive earthquakes (measuring 8.0 or more) only happen about once a year.

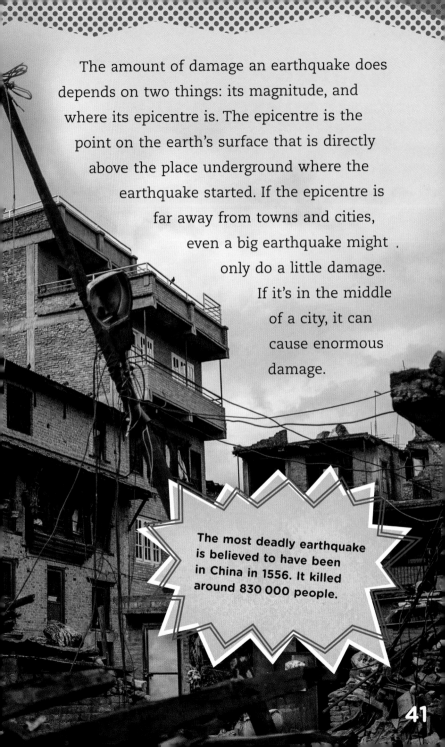

The amount of damage an earthquake does depends on two things: its magnitude, and where its epicentre is. The epicentre is the point on the earth's surface that is directly above the place underground where the earthquake started. If the epicentre is far away from towns and cities, even a big earthquake might only do a little damage. If it's in the middle of a city, it can cause enormous damage.

The most deadly earthquake is believed to have been in China in 1556. It killed around 830 000 people.

Where do earthquakes happen?

Earthquakes can happen anywhere in the world, at any time of year, but most happen in three main areas.

The biggest area runs from Chile in South America all the way to New Zealand. More than three-quarters of the world's biggest earthquakes happen in this zone.

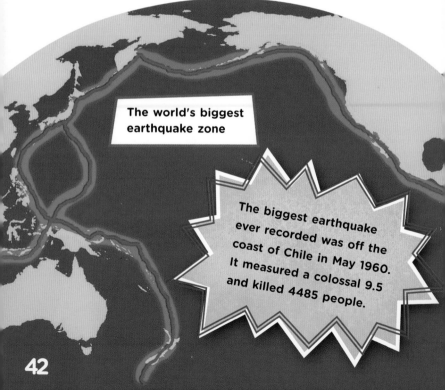

The world's biggest earthquake zone

The biggest earthquake ever recorded was off the coast of Chile in May 1960. It measured a colossal 9.5 and killed 4485 people.

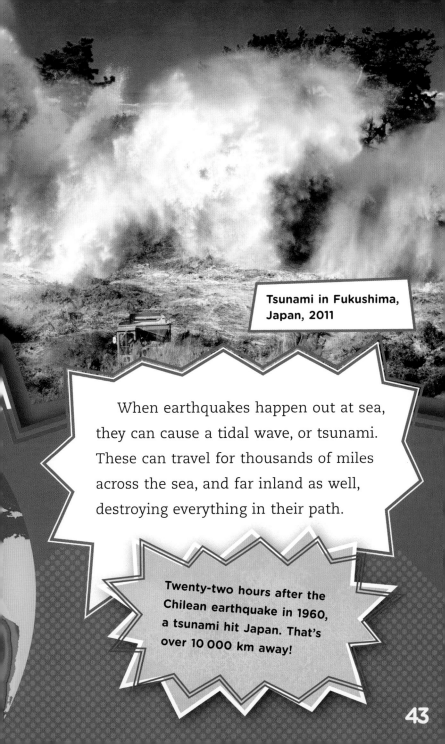

Tsunami in Fukushima, Japan, 2011

When earthquakes happen out at sea, they can cause a tidal wave, or tsunami. These can travel for thousands of miles across the sea, and far inland as well, destroying everything in their path.

Twenty-two hours after the Chilean earthquake in 1960, a tsunami hit Japan. That's over 10 000 km away!

Glossary

vibration   shaking from an earthquake

seismometer   the instrument that measures
the strength of earthquakes

There are earthquakes on the moon as well, known as 'moonquakes'. They're usually smaller than ours and happen a lot less often.

ROCKING LEON'S WORLD

BY JOANNA NADIN
ILLUSTRATED BY ADRIANA SANTOS

BEFORE READING

Setting the scene

Have you ever watched a film or read a comic about a superhero saving the day? Have you ever wished that you could be that hero? Leon, the boy in this story, is longing for that sort of excitement – but will it ever happen?

Prepare to read

Read page 47. What do you know about Leon?

Use the expert tip:

■ **Predict** How likely is it that something out of the ordinary will happen to him?

Challenge word

besides – and another thing
Find this word on page 51. Read it in its sentence and check that you understand what it means.

ROCKING LEON'S WORLD

Chapter 1

Leon lived in an ordinary house, in an ordinary street, in an ordinary town.

After school on Mondays, Leon played football with his mates. On Wednesday evenings, he went swimming with his dad. Most days he read comics, walked his dog, Chops, and wished something extraordinary would happen.

It never did, though.

Leon wanted life to be like it was in comics or on TV. He wanted strange and dangerous aliens to land in the park, and try to scoop everyone up to outer space in a flying saucer. He wanted a terrifying tiger to escape from the zoo and prowl the streets by night, licking its hungry lips. He wanted an enormous earthquake to shake the ground so that buildings wobbled, the ground cracked open, and the school itself fell down. Most of all, he wanted to be a superhero and save everyone from the aliens or tiger or earthquake with his secret powers.

However, the last time Leon looked, he didn't have any secret powers – no flame-throwing fingers, or X-ray eyes, or even a nice pair of invisibility boots. There were no strange and dangerous aliens in the park either, just pigeons. There were no terrifying tigers prowling the streets by night, just next door's cat, Gerald. Worse still, there hadn't been an earthquake for years, not even a tiny one. Not unless you counted the noise Sasha made stamping around the house looking for her gymnastics kit.

"You're loopy, Leon," she would say to him as she stormed past. "Nothing exciting is ever going to happen around here."

"You're not loopy," said Mum. "But Sasha's right. The most interesting thing to happen on our road was when Mrs McGinty at number 43 got new curtains."

Even Dad agreed. "You'll be waiting a long time for an earthquake, Leon," he said. "Besides, you wouldn't like it if we did get one, not really."

But Leon thought he *would* like it. And besides, he knew exactly what to do – he'd read about it in a book. He had to drop to the ground, crawl under a table and hold on until it was over. So Leon carried a bottle of water with him, and taped biscuits under the tops of all the tables in the house, just in case.

Chops found one of Leon's biscuits and ate it.

Sasha found one and gave it to Chops.

Mum found one and told Leon he had to stop wasting food and wasting time wondering about something that was never going to happen. Then she gave the biscuit to Chops.

"You'll be sorry when the earthquake comes," said Leon. "You'll all be sorry." He stormed off to his bedroom in a huff.

Yet as he lay on his bed, Leon wasn't sure
he even believed himself anymore. Why
would an earthquake hit their ordinary house,
on their ordinary street, in their ordinary
town? Mum was right: nothing exciting ever
happened round here, and it would most
probably stay that way forever.

So Leon sighed a massive sigh and began
to read a comic.

ROCKING LEON'S WORLD

Chapter 2

BEFORE READING

Prepare to read

What did you predict would happen in this chapter?

Read page 57. *What did Leon feel? What do you think it means?*

Use the expert tip:

■ **Think and remember** Remember what you have read before about earthquakes to help you understand what a tremor would feel like.

Challenge word

drill

This word has two meanings:

  1 a tool for making holes

  2 a training exercise, e.g. a fire drill.

Find the word on page 61 and read it in a sentence.

Can you work out which definition is correct?

Chapter 2

Leon was just getting to the part of the comic where the dastardly villain Evil Weevil was about to destroy Fantastic Sam's super scooter, when he felt it. It was just a little tremor at first.

Probably Sasha mucking around again, he thought to himself. *It'll stop soon.* He went back to his comic.

It was calm for a while and then another tremor came, bigger this time – the water in the bottle on Leon's bed was rippling. His marble collection clattered in a glass jar on a shelf.

"Mum?" shouted Sasha from down the hall. "What's happening?"

"No idea," replied Mum. "Maybe they're knocking the garden walls down at number 23."

"Or building an extension at number 27?" suggested Sasha.

"It's nothing to worry about," said Mum. "It won't happen again."

Then another tremor came, and Chops started barking.

And that's when Leon knew: no one was knocking down a wall, or building an extension. And this definitely was something to worry about. This was an EARTHQUAKE! And it was happening right here, at his house, on his street, in his town.

"Mum!" he yelled when he got into the kitchen. "Turn off the cooker!"

"But I'm heating soup for tea," she protested. "It's tomato and asparagus. Your favourite."

Tomato and asparagus was indeed Leon's favourite, but now was not the time for soup. Now was the time for some superhero action. Or at least to remember everything he'd read in his earthquake book.

"Listen to me," he said, as the plates on the table began to hop. "And listen carefully. This is not a drill."

"What's happening?" wailed Sasha, who was wobbling like a very tall jelly.

"I don't know!" replied Mum, who was holding on to Sasha, and wobbling like an even taller jelly.

"It's an earthquake," replied Leon. "Just do as I say and you'll be fine."

"First of all, drop to the ground on your hands and knees."

They all dropped.

"Then crawl under the table," said Leon.

They all crawled under the table, including Chops, who thought this was a brilliant game.

"Now hold on," said Leon.

They all held on tight to the table legs. All around them, plates and bowls crashed to the floor, and cutlery clanged around.

Before long, the delicious smell of Mum's tomato and asparagus soup wafted past. Leon knew they couldn't move until he was sure there were no after-tremors, but he suddenly felt incredibly hungry. He reached under the top of the table and pulled something down. "Here," he said. "It's chocolate."

They all finished the biscuit, and Leon's bottle of water, just as the quaking stopped.

Then they cleared up the mess, and everything went back to normal.

Or almost normal.

"Well, I don't suppose we'll see one of those again," said Mum.

"Not round here," agreed Sasha.

Yet, the very next day, Leon found biscuits taped under the tables, and smiled quietly to himself. Maybe aliens would land, or a tiger would get loose after all …

DINO DAD

BY ALI SPARKES
ILLUSTRATED BY CHLOE DOUGLASS

BEFORE READING

Setting the scene

People can get stuck in quicksand, which is deep, wet, loose sand that sucks in anything that steps on it or falls into it. It looks just like flat, watery sand so it is important to look out for warning signs on beaches that alert you to the danger.

In this story, we meet Frankie and his family again. Find out what happens when Frankie encounters quicksand.

Prepare to read

Read page 67. *What do you think is unusual about Frankie's dad?*

Use the expert tip:

■ **Ask a question** *What else would you like to know about Frankie's dad?* Think of your own question and look out for the answer while you are reading.

Challenge word

thrashed around
Find these words on page 71. What do you think they mean?

DINO DAD

Chapter 1

There was crocodile poo on the breakfast
table again.

"Daaad!" wailed Frankie. "I'm trying to eat
my Coco Crispies ... the poo is putting me off!"

"Don't make such a fuss," said Dad,
kneeling over a *huge* thigh bone on the
kitchen floor. "That crocodile dung is a
million years old. It doesn't smell of anything."

Frankie didn't agree. The poo smelt old and musty ... or maybe it was *Dad* who smelt old and musty. He spent so much time with old and musty things, after all. Frankie's dad studied fossils. It's what he did for a job. He spent most of his life digging up the prehistoric bones – and poos – of animals that walked the earth millions of years ago.

Frankie's best friends, Will and Rosi, thought it was an exciting job. They even had a name for Frankie's dad – Dino Dad. It was easy for them – *they* didn't have to live in a house full of old bones. Or look at crocodile poo while they ate Coco Crispies.

Mum came in. "Ooh, that's a nice bit of diplodocus you've got there," she said.

Frankie sighed. Anybody else's mum would have shouted: "WHAT is that stinky chunk of dinosaur doing in here?"

"Isn't it beautiful?" said Dad. "Its owner died in a swamp, so it's been almost perfectly preserved!"

Mum sighed. "What a sad end ... drowning in mud."

"Can you drown in mud?" asked Frankie. "It looks too gloopy."

"Dinosaurs often died in mud, or quicksand or tar pits," said Dad. "That's where we find most of our dinosaur fossils. These creatures might have been big, but they weren't brainy. Once they got stuck they did exactly the wrong thing. They thrashed around to free themselves and made everything much worse."

Frankie gave up on his Coco Crispies.

"So – are you and Will and Rosi coming to the beach with me, then?" asked Dad.

"YES!" cried Frankie.

Two hours later, they all got out of Dad's car.

"Why don't we ever come here on sunny days?" asked Rosi, zipping up her anorak.

"We don't want sun!" said Dino Dad, cheerily. "The best time for fossil hunting is winter. There was a big storm here yesterday – the sea was battering the cliffs. That loosens the clay and reveals fossils."

Dad went off with his hammer and chisel, and told the children to stay by the rock pools. He wanted them to keep away from the stream that trickled down the cliff and spread out watery fingers towards the sea.

The children investigated the rock pools for a while, and then they kicked Will's football around. Frankie passed to Rosi, Rosi passed to Will, and Will took a run-up and gave the ball an almighty kick. It flew high into the air, and of course, it landed exactly where it shouldn't – right on the flat, watery sand by the stream.

"You can't go over there," yelled Rosi, as Will ran after it. "Remember, Frankie's dad said."

But Will didn't hear her. So Frankie ran after him, towards the flat stretch of the beach by the stream.

Thirty seconds later, they were both up to their knees in quicksand.

DINO DAD

Chapter 2

BEFORE READING

Prepare to read

Read page 77. What would it be like to be stuck in quicksand?

Use the expert tips:

Visualize – form a picture in your mind Read page 77 again. What could Frankie and Will see, hear and touch? How do you think they were feeling?

Predict What might they do next?

Challenge word

reassuringly – in a way that makes you feel more confident Find this word on page 83. Can you work out what it means?

Chapter 2

Frankie and Will were stuck in quicksand. They looked down. They had sunk up to their knees in the cold, brown, wet sand. Frankie tried to pull his feet up out of it, but the sand just made a rude sucking noise and wouldn't let go. His knees disappeared.

"I'm stuck!" yelled Will. "Rosi – pull me out!"

"NO!" yelled Frankie. "DON'T! Don't come any closer, Rosi."

"No chance of that!" said Rosi, standing on a lump of rock. She took off her anorak and swung it around by one sleeve. Then she hurled one end of it towards Will.

He managed to grab the sleeve. "Hold tight!" yelled Rosi. Then, using both hands, she pulled the anorak towards her and Will came with it. Well – half of Will came with it. His top half. The bottom half stayed right where it was and then – SPLAT!

Will was face down in the mud.

"Rosi – you'd better go and get my dad," said Frankie. He could see Dad poking about near the foot of the cliffs.

"BLEURGH!" said Will. His face was covered in brown gloop. He managed to push himself up but now he was sitting in the quicksand and sinking to his waist.

"STOP MOVING!" yelled Frankie. "KEEP STILL!"

"YES!" shouted Dad, as he ran towards them with Rosi. "KEEP STILL – and LIE DOWN!"

"Lie *down*?" squeaked Will.

"Yes – unless you *want* to become a fossil, dug up a million years from now," said Dino Dad. "Frankie, you too. Remember the diplodocus in the swamp. Lie back very slowly."

Frankie realized what Dad meant. He didn't want to end up as a specimen in a museum in a million years' time. It felt weird and scary, but he gently sat on the mud and then lay back on it. The cold, sandy soup squelched behind his ears.

Yet Will was still struggling against the wet sand. "Do as Dad says," said Frankie. "He may be obsessed with crocodile poo, but he knows what he's talking about. It's the movement which makes you sink. Just like the dinosaurs in the swamps and tar pits."

Will gave a little whimper and slowly eased himself on to his back.

"Imagine you're floating in a swimming pool," said Dad. "You can swim out on your backs ... but in slow motion. No fast movements."

Frankie realized with relief that he wasn't sinking anymore. The quicksand was turning to *slow* sand beneath him. It wasn't slurping and bubbling now.

"VERY VERY SLOWLY ..." said Dad, and Frankie and Will waved their arms across the surface centimetre by centimetre. Their legs began to rise up, little by little.

It took them half an hour to swim, slow as snails, until they reached the stony part of the beach. With Dad's help, they managed to get out and on to the rocks, which felt reassuringly solid.

"I've never been so happy to see a pile of old stones in my life!" said Frankie, shivering.

Dino Dad smiled. "I knew you'd come round to my point of view eventually," he said.

Dad got towels out of the car and they all dried off and changed their clothes. Then they went for fish and chips to warm up.

This time, when Dino Dad plonked a bag of ancient bones on the table next to the ketchup, Frankie didn't say *a word* …

BY ALI SPARKES

BEFORE READING

Setting the scene

Dinosaurs lived on earth millions of years ago – long before there were any people around to see them. Even so, it is still possible to find clues and build up a surprisingly detailed picture of how the dinosaurs lived and died. Read on to find out more.

Prepare to read

What do you know already about dinosaurs?

Read page 87. What does it tell you about what to expect in this text?

Use the expert tips:

■ **Predict** and **Ask a question** What do you expect to find out? Think of your own question about dinosaurs and look out for that information as you are reading.

Challenge word

technically – according to the strict meaning of something
Find this word on page 93. Read it in its sentence and check that you understand what it means.

Dazzling Dinosaur DISCOVERIES

People have been digging up the bones of dinosaurs for centuries. These bones have turned into a kind of stone over millions of years underground. They give us clues to what prehistoric creatures looked like. Some of the bones even tell us how the creatures died.

Want to see some of the BEST fossils ever found? Turn the page!

dinosaur combat

These bones were discovered in the Gobi Desert in Mongolia in 1971. Two types of dinosaur were fighting to the death. They were a velociraptor and a protoceratops. The two dinosaurs seem evenly matched – they are both roughly two metres long and half a metre high.

Dinosaur experts say the velociraptor attacked first, sinking its deadly curved claw into the protoceratops. It was a carnivore (a meat eater) and probably wanted to eat the protoceratops for dinner. But even though the protoceratops was a herbivore (a plant eater) it fought back hard. It appears to have bitten through the velociraptor's arm, breaking it.

How did they get frozen in time like this for millions of years? Experts think they were caught in a landslide and buried before they could escape. This all happened about 74 million years ago.

The duelling dinosaurs of Montana

In 2006, a team of fossil hunters found this fight scene in Montana, USA. It is believed to be between a tyrannosaurus and a ceratopsian. These are quite small dinosaurs – less than three metres in height – and the tyrannosaurus is thought by some to be a baby tyrannosaurus rex. One of its razor-sharp teeth was found buried in the skull of the plant-eating ceratopsian.

An artist's impression of the dinosaurs

Experts aren't sure how the dinosaurs became fixed in this position forever. It's likely that the dinosaurs were buried in an earthquake – but they'd already killed each other before it struck.

The first flying dinosaur

In 1860, this discovery rocked the world. Found in a quarry in southern Germany, it was the first evidence of a dinosaur bird.

It's an archaeopteryx – a prehistoric bird with feathers – and *teeth*.

This creature has three clawed fingers, almost like a hand, on each wing. It also has a long string of tail bones. No bird alive today has clawed fingers, teeth or a tail like that. It's believed that no bird before the archaeopteryx had feathers.

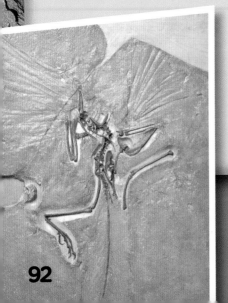

Many people see this as the 'missing link' between prehistoric flying reptiles and the birds we know today.

A complete ichthyosaur fossil

The sea 'dinosaur'

In 1811, Joseph Anning discovered a one-metre-long skull near the sea in Dorset, in the UK. His sister Mary found the rest of the skeleton a few months later. Together, the brother and sister had discovered the first complete skeleton of an ichthyosaur.

The name 'ichthyosaur' means 'fish lizard', so it will come as no surprise that this was a sea-dwelling creature. Although it lived at the same time as the dinosaurs, it technically wasn't a dinosaur. In fact, it looked a bit like a dolphin.

Precious poo

Believe it or not, fossilized poo is highly prized. You can buy these prehistoric droppings for your collection – some people even wear them as jewellery! They are called 'coprolites'.

The world's largest collection of coprolites was counted in the South Florida Museum in America in 2015. Two fossil experts added up all the poos and made a Guinness World Record. There were 1277 coprolites – sent in from eight countries around the world.

Coprolites are very useful because they tell us a lot about what dinosaurs were eating millions of years ago.